MW00889223

Dedicated to Princess Jewel Ruth
with much love.

This book is fantastic. I love the concept and
think it is beautiful! As a mother too, I like
that it guides me on how to introduce the
concept of gratitude to my children.
-Dr Julie Gray, General Practitioner &
Lifestyle Medicine Physician

REVIEW

Are your kids not into normal kids' books or tired of them? Could they be kinder and benefit from more friends?

If the answer to either of those questions is 'yes', consider getting them 'Myra the grumpy puppy and wise Old Dimple' by Dr Adaeze Ifezulike MBE.

This is a beautifully illustrated and accessible allegorical book for 4-9 year olds. Freddie (9) found it 'interesting' and 'different to other books'.

The characters were engaging with Myra 'cute' and Old Dimple 'cuddly'. After reading a sample, kids will want to read the whole thing!

The book encourages reflection and positivity, and we all need more of that. I strongly encourage parents to consider this for presents but also treats.

Dr Fraser Birrell
Editor-in-Chief, Lifestyle Medicine
Consultant & Senior Lecturer in Rheumatology.

PROLOGUE

Myra walked back home with her head and tail down. She was unhappy again. The other puppies didn't want to play with her because they thought she was too grumpy. It wasn't her fault the sun was shining down more than usual, and the heat made her snappy. Myra didn't like the sun.

"Humph! It's their loss anyway. It's not like I wanted to play with them," she grumbled.

"Myra, why the long face?"

Myra looked up and saw Old Dimple. He was much older than her and liked to talk about life. She mumbled and looked down again.

"Well?" Old Dimple pressed.

"The other puppies didn't want to play with me and called me grumpy," Myra frowned. "It's not my fault the sun was shining too bright!"

Old Dimple smiled, "Do you want to know something interesting, Myra?"

"Sure."

"There's something called the light of life."

PROLOGUE

"The light of life?" Myra looked at Old Dimple. He was a very wise dog, but sometimes Myra thought he was just loony.

"Yes, the light of life and it brightens up every time you're grateful. But it dims when you're grumpy."

"How will that help me make friends?" Myra frowned again.

"Do you want to be happy as well as make friends?" Old Dimple asked, and Myra nodded. "Then I want you to try and be grateful for thirty days. Look at the things around you and find something to be grateful for each day, little Myra."

"Thirty days?" Myra repeated in surprise.

Old Dimple simply smiled and went on his way.

Myra continued on her way home too. Her grumpiness was now replaced by thoughtfulness.

She was going to look for things to be grateful for in the next thirty days. That way, she would become happy and have lots of friends.

Day 1

Myra skidded to a stop and saw her food was already placed down for her. She had just run from the field and was very hungry. She wanted to eat all her food as quickly as she could so she could get back to the field and play.

She looked across the lawn and saw Old Dimple. She waved at him.

"About to eat, little Myra?"

"Yes." She nodded eagerly.

"Good food keeps our bodies strong and healthy," Old Dimple smiled and walked away.

Myra looked down at her food. It looked really nice. As she ate, she felt grateful for the food and how happy it made her feel.

Circle the day: Mon Tues Wed Thurs Fri Sat Sun

Think of the last meal you ate.
What did you like best about it?

Today I am GRATEFUL for

....

....

Day 2

Myra was thirsty after running after butterflies for hours. She rushed to the pond to drink some water.

"Hey there, Myra," Old Dimple greeted. He had come to drink water too. "I'm super thirsty."

"Me too."

"The body needs water to work well," Old Dimple grinned.

Myra looked at the water. If water ever disappeared and she had none to drink, she would be very sad. Water made her happy, and she was grateful for the water as she drank.

Circle the day: Mon Tues Wed Thurs Fri Sat Sun

Think about all you can do with water.

What do you like best about water?

Today I am GRATEFUL for ....

Day 3

It was nighttime, and Myra was getting ready to go to bed. As she lay on the blanket and stared at the roof of her kennel, she remembered what Old Dimple once said.

"A good roof keeps you warm and dry."

There was no leak in Myra's roof tonight. She stared at the roof with a smile because even when it was raining outside, the roof kept her warm and dry. She was grateful for the roof over her head.

Circle the day: Mon Tues Wed Thurs Fri Sat Sun

Think about your room. What do you like about it?

Today I am GRATEFUL for

....

....

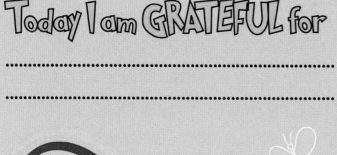

Day 4

Myra enjoyed playing in the fields and rolling in the grass but sometimes became grumpy when she had to take a bath afterwards.

One day, she decided she wouldn't play in the grass anymore. "Myra, what's wrong?" Old Dimple asked.

"I won't play in the grass anymore, so I don't have to bathe."

"Little Myra, play in the grass while you can; you won't like it as much when you grow up."

That night, Myra thought about what Old Dimple said. She hardly saw him or her parents play in the grass anymore. She did enjoy rolling in the grass. For today, she felt grateful for being able to play and roll around in the grass, even if it meant having to take a bath afterwards.

Circle the day: Mon Tues Wed Thurs Fri Sat Sun
Think about when you last played on the field.
What did you like best about it?

Today I am GRATEFUL for ....

Day 5

Myra disliked bathing. She whined and complained when it was time to bathe. She always struggled and gave mom a hard time. But Old Dimple convinced her otherwise.

"Bath time is also bonding time!"

When the next bath time came around, Myra smiled at mom and didn't complain for the very first time. She was grateful for bath time to bond with mom. She felt happy when her mom gave her a hug for behaving well at bath time.

Circle the day: Mon Tues Wed Thurs Fri Sat Sun

Think about bath time. What do you like best about it?

Today I am GRATEFUL for

....

....

Day 6

The other puppies allowed Myra to join their game when they saw she wasn't snappy or grumbling like usual. Myra learned she had to be nice to everyone if she wanted to play with them. She remembered what Old Dimple said.

"The only way to have a friend is to be friendly."

Myra was grateful for her new friends and was very happy playing with them.

Circle the day: Mon Tues Wed Thurs Fri Sat Sun

Think about your friends.
What do you like best about your friends?

Today I am GRATEFUL for ....

....

Day 7

Myra didn't always enjoy school or the homework her teacher gave at the end of the day. As she grumbled on her way home, she saw Old Dimple under a tree.

"Hey there, Old Dimple."

"How are you, Myra? I saw you grumbling from a mile away. You know it dims your light of life."

"I got homework from my teacher."

"That's not so bad. Homework will help make you successful in the future. Remember, A teacher helps you learn lots of useful things."

When Myra got home, she wasn't upset anymore. She wanted to be successful and was grateful for her teacher.

Circle the day: Mon Tues Wed Thurs Fri Sat Sun

Think about your teachers.

What do you like best about teachers?

....

....

Day 8

Myra spent her afternoon chasing butterflies through the flowers. When she finished playing, she met Old Dimple on her way home. Later that night, she thought about something the wise dog said.

"Imagine a world without butterflies; it would be a world without colour."

It would truly be a colourless world without butterflies. That night, Myra felt thankful for all the butterflies she got to play with during the day.

Circle the day: Mon Tues Wed Thurs Fri Sat Sun

Think of all the things you play with.
Which one do you like best? Why?

Today I am GRATEFUL for ....

Day 9

Before bed, Myra's daddy or mommy would read nice stories to her, and she would sleep off as they read. As her mother read about a giraffe and a lion that night, Myra remembered what Old Dimple once said.

"Bedtime stories help you have nice dreams when you sleep." Myra closed her eyes and smiled. She was grateful for reading time with her parents.

Circle the day: Mon Tues Wed Thurs Fri Sat Sun
Do you like bedtime stories?
Which ones do you like best?

Today I am GRATEFUL for

....

....

Day 10

It was the holidays. The house was full of Myra's siblings and cousins. They were a noisy bunch, laughing and singing together. Myra enjoyed playing with her siblings and cousins all day long. When the time came for them to leave, she was sad. She realised Old Dimple was right when he said, "Family is precious. If you have them, be cheerful that you do." Although she missed them, she was grateful for her family.

Circle the day: Mon Tues Wed Thurs Fri Sat Sun

Think about your family.

What do you like best about them?

Today I am GRATEFUL for ....

....

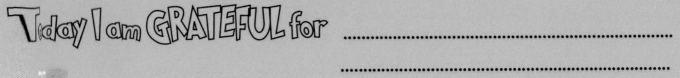

Day 11

Myra fell sick after playing in the pond for too long. As she sneezed and coughed, she remembered the days when she wasn't sneezing or coughing. She missed those days. Most especially, she was grateful for good health.

"Be grateful for being able to breathe and eat well because all you will think about when you are sick is those good days."
—Old Dimple

Circle the day: Mon Tues Wed Thurs Fri Sat Sun

How did you feel the last time you were ill?

Today I am GRATEFUL for

....

....

Day 12

It was summer, and Myra could go to the hills and pond all day long. Old Dimple told her, "Each season has something special to give us. Learn to be thankful for each season." Myra had not thought about how nice it was to have summer. She could move around, play with the butterflies and run with friends. For today, Myra was grateful for summer.

Circle the day: Mon Tues Wed Thurs Fri Sat Sun

Think about winter and summer.
Which one do you like best? Why?

Today I am GRATEFUL for

....

....

Day 13

Myra didn't know what to be grateful for when she woke up. She still didn't know what to be thankful for as bedtime came. Then she remembered how exciting school had been. She had enjoyed making crafts out of paper.

Old Dimple often said, "Sit in school for a few hours, and you will learn about numbers, plants and arts. Isn't it amazing? To learn so much in just a day."

Myra was grateful she could go to school and learn new things every day.

Circle the day: Mon Tues Wed Thurs Fri Sat Sun

What do you enjoy about school?
What did you learn today?

Today I am GRATEFUL for ....

Day 14

Myra loved eating cake on special days. It was her friend's birthday, and she got a slice of cake. Cake made her very happy and grateful, which made her light of life brighten like a star in the sky. As Old Dimple once said, "Eating a slice of cake is like tasting a slice of happiness."

Myra wasn't allowed to eat cake often. Mom said it was not healthy to eat it very often. So she was grateful for the cake she got to eat today.

Circle the day: Mon Tues Wed Thurs Fri Sat Sun

Think about the last birthday party you went to. What nice things did you eat?

Today I am GRATEFUL for

....

....

Day 15

Once a month, Myra would go to the town's campfire and run around the fire happily with her friends. They loved to see the shadows the flames made and enjoyed slices of smoked fish Dimple gave them.

"No better bonding time than around the campfire!" Old Dimple would tell them.

Myra was grateful for the campfire and that she could enjoy it with her friends.

Circle the day: Mon Tues Wed Thurs Fri Sat Sun

Think about the last time you had an outing with your friends. What did you enjoy about it?

Today I am GRATEFUL for ....

....

Day 16

After playing on the fields with the other puppies, Myra found a cool spot underneath the trees and had a nap.

"Naptime helps your body stay strong."

—Old Dimple

Myra was grateful for nap time and how strong she felt after napping.

Circle the day: Mon Tues Wed Thurs Fri Sat Sun

Think about when you had a nap.
How did you feel when you woke up?

Today I am GRATEFUL for

....

....

Day 17

During break time, a puppy pushed Myra off the swing. She landed with a whimper. A teacher made the other puppy say 'sorry' to Myra. The puppy was sorry, but Myra still wanted to push the puppy off the swing as well!

Then she remembered Old Dimple and something he said in the past. "It's nice to forgive others when they are sorry for what they have done."

So Myra forgave the other puppy, and they played on the swings together. They became good friends. Myra was grateful that she was able to forgive the other puppy.

Circle the day: Mon Tues Wed Thurs Fri Sat Sun

Think about when you hurt someone.
Did you remember to say you were sorry?

Today I am GRATEFUL for

....

....

Day 18

Myra felt happy when she went to the field that morning. Everyone said she was having a good hair day. Her hair wasn't fuzzy, and her coat was shiny.

According to Old Dimple, "Happiness is a good hair day!"

Myra was grateful for her good hair day.

Circle the day: Mon Tues Wed Thurs Fri Sat Sun

Think about your hair.
What do you like about it?

Today I am GRATEFUL for

....

....

Day 19

Myra loved chocolates and candy bars. She couldn't eat them every day because Mom said it wasn't good for her body. But on the days she could, she enjoyed them. Today was one of those days, and she was grateful for chocolates!
Old Dimple saw her snacking and chuckled.
"Chocolate is a delicious piece of happiness in the mouth."

Circle the day: Mon Tues Wed Thurs Fri Sat Sun

Think about the snacks you eat.
Which ones do you enjoy best?

Today I am GRATEFUL for

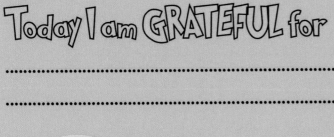

....

....

Day 20

"Walks are great, aren't they, little Myra?" Old Dimple asked. Myra was taking a long walk with the wise dog. She nodded. "I guess so, Old Dimple."

"Our brains work well when we go on regular walks," Old Dimple said.

Later on, Myra thought about Old Dimple's words and found he was correct. She had practised her numbers and alphabets as they walked. Today, Myra was grateful for the joy of taking a walk and how well it made her brain work.

Circle the day: Mon Tues Wed Thurs Fri Sat Sun

Think about the last time you went for a walk.
What did you see or do?

Today I am GRATEFUL for ....

Day 21

Playtime was something Myra enjoyed. If she wasn't running in the meadows or playing catch with her friends, she went swimming. When winter came, sometimes it was too cold, and she couldn't go out as much.

So as she ran through the warm meadows with her friends, she was grateful for playtime.

"Playtime helps your body stay strong."
—Old Dimple

 **Circle the day:** Mon Tues Wed Thurs Fri Sat Sun

Think about playtime. Which play do you enjoy most?

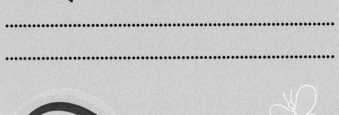 **Today I am GRATEFUL for**

....

....

Day 22

When Myra wasn't outdoors, she was indoors playing with her toys. Today, Myra played with her toys and had a lot of fun. She was grateful for all the toys her mom bought for her to play with. She felt really happy.

Old Dimple was right when he said, "A toy a day keeps the grumpiness and sadness away!"

Circle the day: Mon Tues Wed Thurs Fri Sat Sun

Think about your toys.
What is the name of your favourite toy?

Today I am GRATEFUL for

....

....

Day 23

The park was another spot Myra loved playing at. She could swing and jump on the jungle gym. Old Dimple said he didn't have any swings to swing from when he was younger. That made Myra sad, but it also made her grateful for the lovely park near her home.

And as Old Dimple usually said, "Don't forget to be grateful for the little things as well as the big things."

Circle the day: Mon Tues Wed Thurs Fri Sat Sun

Think about the fun you had at the park.
What did you like best?

Today I am GRATEFUL for

....

....

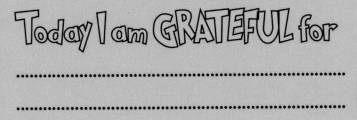

Day 24

Myra liked Break time because it was when she could play with her friends on the swings. She was glad when the Break time bell rang, and she ran out to the playground. As she laughed with her friends during the break, her light of life brightened. She was grateful for break time.

"When I was in school, I had two favourite times, lunch and break time," said Old Dimple

Circle the day: Mon Tues Wed Thurs Fri Sat Sun

Think about break time. Who do you play with?
What do you like to do?

Today I am GRATEFUL for ....

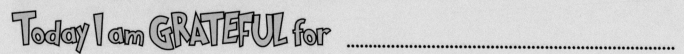

Day 25

"Isn't air such a beautiful thing, little Myra?" Old Dimple asked Myra as they drank water from the pond.

"I can't see air, Old Dimple." Myra giggled.

"Just because you can't see the air doesn't mean it's not there," Old Dimple smiled.

"Air keeps us up and moving."

When Old Dimple had gone, Myra took a deep breath and let it out. She couldn't see air, but she could sure feel it. Myra was grateful for the air she got to breathe in and out every day.

Circle the day: Mon Tues Wed Thurs Fri Sat Sun

Take a deep breath in and out. Do you know air keeps us alive?

I am grateful for

....

....

Day 26

During picnics, Myra's mom would lay down blankets. The warm ground would heat the blankets, making them warm. Myra loved laying down on the warm blankets and napping. Today was a picnic day, and Myra was grateful for the warm blankets beneath her. She was thankful for all the nice picnic food they brought to eat.

"A warm blanket and picnic food make a puppy happy!" Old Dimple said.

Circle the day: Mon Tues Wed Thurs Fri Sat Sun
TThink about the last time you went on a picnic.
What did you like best?

Today I am GRATEFUL for

Day 27

On rainy days, Myra watched the raindrops splash on the ground. Today was a rainy day. She wished the rain would stop so she could go outside to play. Then she remembered one of Old Dimple's sayings. "Without the rain, there would be no flowers."

Myra loved flowers, so she decided to be grateful for the rain that brought the beautiful flowers.

Circle the day: Mon Tues Wed Thurs Fri Sat Sun

Think of the last rainy day.
What fun did you enjoy inside the house?

Today I am GRATEFUL for

....

....

Day 28

Old Dimple and some of the other dogs sang songs in the evening. All the puppies sang along. As Old Dimple sang, Myra remembered what he told her earlier, "Without music, life would not be fun!"

Myra sang along with the other puppies. She was happy and felt grateful for the music that made life fun.

Circle the day: Mon Tues Wed Thurs Fri Sat Sun

When last did you sing a song?
What is your favourite song?

Today I am GRATEFUL for ....

Day 29

Myra was a good dancer and loved dancing. Whenever the music came on, she would dance till her little feet ached. She danced to the songs playing and was grateful for being able to dance.

"Dancing makes the heart merry", Old Dimple had said. Myra felt quite merry as she danced along.

Circle the day: Mon Tues Wed Thurs Fri Sat Sun

Think about the last time you danced.
How did it make you feel?

Today I am GRATEFUL for

....

....

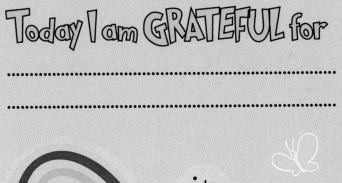

Day 30

Myra never liked the sun. She often grumbled when it shone hard, but Old Dimple told her something which changed her mind about the sun.

"Without the sun, how would we see and feel warm? You can't like the warmth and dislike the sun."

Since then, Myra never grumbled about the sun again. She enjoyed the warmth and would miss it during the long winter days. It was a hot day today, and for once, Myra was grateful for the sun and all the warmth it provided.

Circle the day: Mon Tues Wed Thurs Fri Sat Sun

Think about a sunny day. What do you enjoy most about it?

Today I am GRATEFUL for

....

EPILOGUE

"Old Dimple, Old Dimple!" Myra called out.

"Whoa there, slow down, little Myra," Old Dimple laughed at the puppy.

"It has been thirty days and I was grateful each day!" Myra smiled, jumping happily.

"That is amazing, My a; you did great."

"My light of life is shining brighter than the sun! I will never be grumpy again, and I will always find a reason to be grateful." Myra promised.

Little Myra stayed true to her words. Through the long winters and storms, she found a reason to be grateful. All the other puppies now loved playing with her. This was how Myra changed from being a grumpy puppy to the most cheerful puppy ever.

The end

Manufactured by Amazon.ca
Bolton, ON

27927696R00021